THE BEST OF

PUGH

2012

9449

Daily Mail

THE BEST OF

PUGH

2012

hamlyn

For Tom and Phoebe

An Hachette UK Company
www.hachette.co.uk

First published in Great Britain in 2011 by Hamlyn,
a division of Octopus Publishing Group Ltd
Endeavour House, 189 Shaftesbury Avenue, London WC2H 8JY
www.octopusbooks.co.uk

ISBN 978-0-60062-334-2

A CIP catalogue record for this book is available from the British Library.

1 3 5 7 9 10 8 6 4 2

Executive Editor: Trevor Davies
Senior Editor: Sybella Stephens
Production: Lucy Carter
Page make up: Dorchester Typesetting Group Ltd
Printed and bound by CPI Group (UK) Ltd, Croydon CR0 4YY

Contents

Health 9

Money and Business 31

Pets and Animals 46

Politics, World and War 57

Royalty 84

Love and Life 88

Sport 140

Weather 150

Jonathan Pugh first studied law, which presented him with hours of doodling practice. After a brief stint as an art teacher, he began his career as a freelance cartoonist in 1987.

In January 2010 he joined the *Daily Mail* as their daily pocket cartoonist after nearly fifteen years at *The Times*.

He was voted the Cartoon Art Trust Pocket Cartoonist of the Year in 1998, 2000, 2001, 2007 and 2010 and was the British Press Awards Cartoonist of the Year in 2001. As well as illustrating several books his work has also appeared in The *Guardian*, The *Independent*, The *Observer*, *Private Eye*, *Country Life* and *The Spectator*. His work also appears weekly in *The Tablet*.

"Do you write your own captions?" is the question I'm most often asked. "Well, yes, I do", I mutter. The next question is usually "Where do you get your ideas from?", which is not quite so easy to answer. Staring at a blank piece of paper wishing I were somewhere else is usually how it starts, followed by a creeping sense of anxiety as it dawns on me that I can't think of anything remotely funny. This teeters on panic as time ticks on and I'm expected to come up with 10–15 ideas, but still can't think of one. The nightmare vision of a gap in tomorrow's newspaper where the pocket cartoon should be and an angry editor is a highly effective way of focusing the mind and eventually – somehow – I manage to find inspiration.

I'll submit a flurry of ideas, cleverly avoiding topics which are impossible to be funny about, like political talks in Northern Ireland and the outbreak of World War III, and stories that

contain terms like 'EU' and 'Monetary Union' that make my eyes glaze over and my brain freeze. But then stories develop or a new one hits and the amorphous nature of the newspaper's priorities shift once more and I'm back to square one and that blank piece of paper.

This may sound like I'm bemoaning my lot, but I'm not, I just thought it would be good to give you an insight into the cartoons' creation as you browse this collection. The fact is it's quite difficult to be funny when the news is dominated by a disaster or give a fresh angle on a perennial story that you've done 30 or 40 cartoons on in the past (think A-level results or another politician's dodgy expenses claim). But I've lost count of how often I've been saved by the quirkier stories – overweight pets or snow in June, a pothole crisis or a shortage of asparagus, the latest diet or madcap invention – which fall into my grateful lap like manna from heaven and remind me how lucky I am to be a cartoonist for a daily newspaper in Britain.

You'll see many types of these cartoons in this compilation. It contains 300 that I thought would amuse you the most. Some are jokes about the big heavyweight stories of the past 18 months and some the most trivial, and a lot in between. Hopefully, they all show how the British, whatever the circumstances, manage to find the lighter side of life.

I hope you enjoy them,

Jonathan Pugh

"*Unfit gene or not, you can still get up and turn the television on*"

Humans have shrunk by 10% … farming may be
to blame

*"I never thought the day would come I'd
leave the meat and eat the gherkin"*

*"How does one tell if these baked beans are
cloned or not?"*

"I can't help you, I'm stuck too!"

Half of our soldiers are overweight, a study claims

"I think it's called cake"

"It makes sense – it leaves more room
for pudding"

"When I was your age I only had two spare tyres"

"Where do I plug in my Xbox?"

"Mum, Dad's had all the roast potatoes again"

"You're in luck, I can't bend down and pick it up either"

"You have to do everything yourself these days…"

"We find it a very good slug deterrent"

More than nine out of ten British sausages contain more salt than a packet of crisps

"Do you take milk with your tea, vicar?"

Goats' milk the latest "superfood"

"I'd say the suspect is aged somewhere between 16 and 70..."

"Can she call you back? She's sitting in the garden waiting to be stung"

"Have you been rubbing it on your tummy again?"

*"I'm getting worried – that's the fifth walk
he's given the dog this morning"*

A great grandfather has become Britain's oldest
father at 76

"Wonderful news! My mother's expected to reach 110!"

"No wonder your mother never suffers"

"Don't ask"

"Good grief! You must be British"

British women are the most overweight in
Western Europe, figures have revealed

*"You're too aggressive! Have you
considered changing your diet?!"*

A study shows that mountain gorillas follow a
low-carbohydrate, high-protein diet similar to
the Atkins plan

"Chicken eggs, not Cadbury creme ones"

"What?!! You've finished them already?!"

"He adores dusting"

Having a pet could cut the risk of children having allergies

"This is the fourth health check you've given me today"

"It's a nasty blister – a bit of disability benefit might make it better"

"You have an itchy nose – I don't think we need to put the undertakers on standby"

Scientists have confirmed that you're often not as ill as you say you are

Red wine bolsters the brain's defences against the
damage of a stroke, say scientists

"Your diagnosis has come through! Your diagnosis has come through!"

"You're grinding your teeth again, dear"

"Hello and goodbye"

Survey reveals GP appointment times are
too short

*"And I always thought it was an apple that
kept the doctor away"*

"How lovely to be miserable when one still has one's health"

"I wish he would have mood swings – he's permanently bad-tempered"

"Can you remember where I put those memory loss pills?"

"George is holding on until the NHS is reformed"

"She's lucky, we had them for 13 years"

"Welcome to Lloyds TSB – to complain politely, press 1; to rant and rave, press 2; to hurl abuse…"

"It went better than I hoped – they lent me a tea bag"

"No need for alarm, dear – it's my bank manager"

"Our bank manager must be an only child"

"It doesn't feel right to pick up a bonus this year... I'll get my chauffeur to do it"

"You've been a failure all year, can't you award yourself a bonus?"

Public outcry as the state-backed lender awards bonuses to its bosses

"Now I'll never get asked to do the flake advert"

"I imagine it's the appeal of a warmer climate"

"What's 'beware of the dog' in Spanish, Chinese and German?"

"On the other hand we don't want people thinking we've been hit by the recession…"

"It's tempting to sell up and buy in Greece"

"There must be another way of helping the Irish economy?!"

"We need women in the boardroom – go and put a skirt on, Phillpot"

British companies are facing the threat of compulsory female quotas in board members

"Perhaps Rosemary would like to go and pick up the inequality report from the foyer"

"Whatever happened to sex equality?"

"It's not perfect but at least no-one can accuse us of discrimination"

Rise in VAT

"Our accountant is recommending we pass away before January 1st 2016"

"Is this tax evasion scheme really worth it?"

Government crackdown on tax evasion

"I understand you're looking for a nine-to-five-minutes-past job"

"I've changed my mind about being a footballer, now I want to be a council fat cat"

1,250 council chiefs earn in excess of £100,000

"I think we need to improve our home delivery system"

Sainsbury's tell their delivery drivers that they don't have to climb higher than the first floor if there is no lift

"I still don't think we should abandon the mobile phone altogether"

"My car's fine but my husband is riddled with faults"

Toyota voluntarily recalls its flagship 'green' car over brake problems

"What luck! No-one can see we're driving a Toyota"

"Thank heavens for that pothole!"

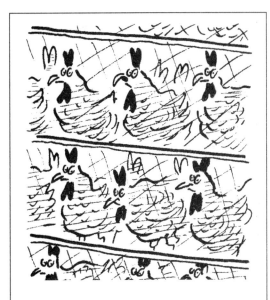

"It's a disgrace how many commuters South West Trains will squeeze into a carriage"

"Thank heavens I met you"

Increasing number of animal lovers making
arrangements to be buried with their pets

"Apart from looking cute do you have any other qualifications?"

After 40 years the Andrex puppy is replaced by a computer-generated version

Rise in posh dog names

One in five of us admit to being too lazy to take
the dog for a walk

"I do wish you'd walk him properly"

Rise in cat obesity

Woman filmed tossing somebody's cat into a
wheelie bin

Scientists claim that pet dogs are smarter than
their feline counterparts

"And in the general knowledge round you've scored a record total of..."

Scientists say that elephants actually do have long memories

"The annoying thing is I hadn't stopped..."

*"You can't say our pond hasn't attracted
any wildlife"*

"Left after the third cabbage…"

Research appears to show that snails have a
strong homing instinct

"You are funny, dear, you do exaggerate"

30-inch rodents seen

"I assure you, it's not me tickling your feet"

"I think the egg may be past its sell-by date"

Best-before dates may be scrapped in an attempt to cut the five million tonnes of food Britons throw out each year

Mother hens are such attentive, caring parents that they 'feel' their chicks' pain

"You spoil that bird"

Boom in sales of bird tables

"It's the slowest computer I've ever known"

Hedgehogs facing extinction

"Thank heavens decking is going out of fashion"

"Are you going to tell Michael Foot about our dress code or am I?"

"Does Lembit Opik count?"

"Tony Blair's running late – he should be here in 45 minutes"

"I miss him being PM – we saw a lot less of him"

"They say the British have over 200 words to describe Alastair Campbell"

Alastair Campbell giving evidence in the Iraq inquiry

"Hang on a sec – have we cleared this invasion with the legal department?"

Iraq inquiry – ministers brushed aside warnings of the legality of the war

"Cameron's Prime Minister Monday, Wednesday and Fridays, and Clegg does Tuesday and Thursdays"

"I hope the Cleggs haven't bagged the best bedroom"

*"An aisle seat or one next to
the Prime Minister?"*

David and Samantha Cameron fly to Spain with
budget airline Ryanair

"Do we pay him or does he pay us?"

"Good heavens, is it elevenses already?"

Labour's culture of excess laid bare as expense claims unveiled

"I wish I could remember which Miliband I swore undying support for…"

"They're so green they've even recycled their pledges from the last election"

"I'm suddenly envious of immigrants who don't understand English"

"It's quite sweet the way grown ups always think a new manifesto will make everything better"

"I don't mind a new diet but this is ridiculous"

Ministers claim feeding cows a healthier diet could reduce their flatulence and help prevent global warming

"I wouldn't have gone on strike if I'd known this was on the telly"

"Do we need a clown for the grandchildren's party?"

"It's time you knew, Penelope – I'm a non-dom"

"A long, long time ago – even before the election campaign had started…"

"Nowadays I worry my children don't watch enough television"

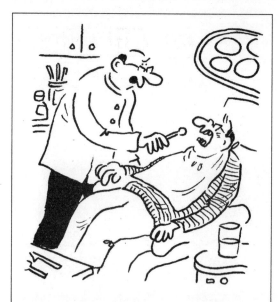

"Dear me, somebody has been swallowing a lot of pre-election sweeteners"

None of the parties achieved the 326 seats
needed for an overall majority in the 2010
UK general election.

Debate over prisoners' voting rights

"At last we'll have somewhere to put all those election pledges"

"Ready ... take aim ... fire!"

"Somehow it's not the same since the budget cuts"

"I wasn't expecting the Arts cuts to be quite so brutal"

"It's hard enough finding one MP to elect, let alone two"

"We're economising this week – it's non-vintage"

"They were worried they wouldn't be able to get Nick Clegg out of Downing Street"

"If your mother's not out of here by the weekend I'm calling the police"

"This is the police – you have me surrounded"

Police cuts

Police pay cut anger

"It's the celery stick and carrot approach"

"Of course we still love you, but not quite so much"

"Don't tell me! I do not want to know!"

Draft legislation to extend maternity leave to
20 weeks full pay

"We've commissioned a large non-
departmental public body to help us"

"I keep worrying about all this talk of double dip"

"Middle of a recession sex boom and you have a double dip!"

"I'll put the kettle on. Call me if another government's toppled"

"Next year if you forget my birthday you can always call the French embassy"

"I admit I was holding the wheel, officer, but my wife was backseat driving"

Police investigate whether it was Chris Huhne or Vicky Pryce who committed a speeding offence

"I'm sorry I ever doubted you, Dudley…"

Liberal MP breaches privacy injunction naming
the footballer alleged to have had a relationship
with Big Brother star, Imogen Thomas.

"I'm afraid he's out – do you want to try him
on his Caribbean number?"

Councillor pay row

"I wonder if that's our bank manager going to work or our councillor?"

"I spy with my little eye something beginning with 'O'..."

BP Gulf of Mexico oil spill

"We've apologised to Miriam O'Reilly and offered her a job on the Antiques Roadshow"

BBC condemned for dropping female journalist
because she was too old

"He says he'll stop fighting for one of the new Apple tablets"

"It's 3a.m. – can we speculate about Carole Middleton's wedding outfit in the morning?"

"Ideally they want a Saturday that doesn't clash with X Factor, Strictly or the football"

"Do you have to tick off every minute to the Royal Wedding?"

"I don't think you need to practise your curtsey, dear"

"Well, I'm very sorry but I'm not happy with the seating plan"

"I was rather hoping for Prince William"

Prince William to fly air-sea rescue helicopters

"He couldn't take any more of Prince Charles moaning about his tax bill"

"Well, I'm not in the mood anymore – you could have got them so much cheaper than Tesco"

Women in their thirties and early forties have
higher sex drives than their younger and
perkier counterparts

Scientists claim it's true that women settle down
for love and men for regular sex

"I'd still prefer a Malteser"

"If we added up every time I'm sure we'd be very nearly there"

"Lack of sex?! Good heavens, have you forgotten our honeymoon?"

Lack of love and lost interest in sex is driving the over-50s to divorce

"We can't put 'don't know' to every question"

A survey reveals that eight out of ten women over the age of 50 think members of the opposite sex no longer notice them

"Actually my wife invented it, whatever it is..."

A study has found evidence of alpha cavewomen

"Ten years ago my wife wouldn't have even touched the remote control"

"Don't worry about George, he's purely decorative"

"We'll leave you two nattering, we're off to the pub"

"Do you have to wear stilts every time we go out?"

"Right, who was Liverpool left-back when they won the FA cup in 1974?"

"Now pause a moment for dramatic effect..."

Psychologists claim the secret of some men's success may be their spouse

"Are we married? I can't remember…"

"Absolute nonsense"

"She says she'll be five minutes – she's just doing her make-up"

One in three women won't step outside without putting on make-up

"Duck, dear, telegraph wire ahead"

"Night night, dear, sleep well"

Women still do the lion's share of domestic duties

FOR GREAT FAMILY LIFE, GO ABROAD

"Where do you suggest I send him?"

"I'll remember to leave mine out next time your mother's here"

"My mother's promised not to knit you a jumper this Christmas"

"A moth's never harmed anybody, dear…"

Recent hot spell has caused an increase in moths

"She'll call you back – she's stuck on the fridge door again"

Mother has mysterious power that means metallic objects stick to her body

"Are you sure offering them tea is the right thing?"

"Are you sure you're from Essex? You sound a bit too posh"

"There must be somebody we know I can look down on?"

"It makes me so angry – no apostrophe again"

"Let me guess – you've got one of those new super-fast washing machines?"

"See? The grass really is greener on the other side"

An extra £100 million to be spent filling pot holes

"Shouldn't you be pushing me, Mum?"

"Mum, you know school doesn't like hemlines above the knee…"

Research tells us that nine out of ten women aim to dress younger than their years

"I'm bound to fail, I haven't done any revision"

"I'm keeping my fingers crossed no secondary school will want me at all"

"You're absolutely positive this is your nearest school?"

"I'm dreading telling my parents how I did in my GCSEs this year"

Deluge of complaints about exam question errors

"Typical teenagers – once one has an A* they all want one"

"I was hoping for £27,000 to get me through university"

"I'm afraid I could only afford a third"

"The problem with Google Streetview is that every road looks the same"

"It's only midday and the Hopkinson's are already having a sherry"

"Tell them we're not going there for lunch
unless they supply a police escort"

"When I said order me something from
Amazon I was hoping for a book"

Amazon launches UK online grocery store

"61 million people in Britain and you still haven't got a friend on Facebook?!"

Soaring cost of car insurance

"I know it's not perfect but think of the money we're saving"

"And all these dots are where we're being overcharged for petrol"

Petrol prices soar across the UK

Parents are kitting their cars out with entertainment equipment to keep their children happy

"Either Lancashire's changed or the
Sat-Nav's faulty again"

"I'm sure that's the same snail that overtook
us at Junction 12"

"You're not wearing a seatbelt and you've got a bit of spinach between your teeth"

"Jump, dear! I can't stop, I'll get a ticket!"

"Come and double the viewing figures"

Viewers desert Daybreak programme in droves

"No, you won't see it from that angle either"

"In that round I'm afraid you only scored
two points"

A BBC Mastermind contestant scores the worst
total in the show's 37-year history

More than half of older viewers believe television
standards have declined

"There's nothing on the telly again tonight"

"Do you want the news read by someone who earns £250,000 or £400,000 a year?"

BBC high salaries row

"The batteries must be going – Terry Wogan sounds very peculiar this morning"

Chris Evans becomes Radio 2's new breakfast show host

"Press 1 to add one ethnic character, 2 to add two ethnic characters, 3 to add…"

Uproar after a producer reveals that ethnic characters are deliberately kept out of the show's storylines

"He'll be a couple of hours, he's just putting the bins out"

"I've forgotten, dear – which one is for nail clippings?"

Nearly 140 local authorities now force householders to sort rubbish into five or more containers

Families face being rationed to 80 bags of rubbish a year

"That's the lifers wing – murderers, rapists
and people who overfilled their
rubbish bins"

"It's wider than it used to be, so they can get all the noughts on"

"Couldn't we pay to use a campsite like everybody else?"

Boom in camping holidays

*"We're making the most of the hosepipe
before the ban kicks in"*

Price of bread soars

"Was that tea a peppermint or
a chamomile?"

Sales of herbal tea have risen by 60% in
just a year

Hollywood fad sends baby food sales booming

Calls for less food packaging

"Is that the bullying helpline?"

"The locally sourced venison sounds tempting…?"

*"No-one burns it to a cinder more
beautifully than you, dear"*

The French are outdone by the British when it
comes to putting a home-cooked meal on the
table at the end of the day

*"That was a lovely risotto, dear, but I might
just leave the rest to fill in the pot
hole outside"*

Sales of risotto rice have soared to record levels

"If this doesn't stop young people binge
drinking nothing will"

"I'm just spending a quiet evening in front
of the box"

Middle-class are more than twice as likely to drink
heavily than those on lower incomes

*"The little brat wants an ice cream, does he?
I'll give him an ice cream..."*

Heston Blumenthal's mustard-flavoured ice cream
launched in Waitrose

"I'll believe it when I see it"

*"Do we want the full-cloned or the
semi-cloned?"*

"There's no need to cry over spilt milk –
we'll buy an identical pint later"

"Don't worry, it's not your mother, it's
a clone"

"Was the giraffe on your mother's side or your father's side?"

"Can't you enter the kitchen like a
normal person?"

"It's done wonders for our marriage"

"Do you want it with or without the stutter?"

A genetic link to stammering has been found by scientists

"Enjoy being grumpy, you've only got fifteen months left"

"Given any thought to what you might like to do for your 100th birthday?"

"I'm still not convinced about this later retirement age"

"And here's a little something, Gran, to buy yourself a treat"

"Okay dear, you can come in now"

"Morning dear"

"I said, darling, what do you think of these
off the peg glasses?"

"They are naughty – this was on four years ago"

"Ssshhh … I'm working"

"The lovely thing is it's not the winning it's the taking part"

"If I fail my GCSEs my Dad's threatened to buy me an England kit"

England have a disastrous World Cup tournament in South Africa

"I find the vuvuzela drowns the irritating
noise of my husband"

"I've silenced the vuvuzelas for you"

"It's not hay fever – it's the football"

England captain John Terry facing revelations
about his personal life

"If you don't want to know the latest sleaze, please look away now"

"It's a lovely transplant but I still prefer you bald"

Wayne Rooney has a hair transplant

"You never sat that close when the football was on"

"For heavens sake, George, please stop ducking"

"I'd hurry up and bring the washing in, dear, it's bound to rain"

"On your marks..."

"Don't let on we've got Olympic tickets, they'll think you've been involved in some genocide"

Regimes in Libya and Zimbabwe request hundreds of Olympic tickets

*"I really don't think a public denial is
necessary, dear"*

*"He's cancelled his Sky subscription – he
misses all the sexist banter"*

Andy Gray is sacked and Richard Keys resigns
from Sky Sports

"You've had four whole years to get ready for this"

"Relax, there's a bank holiday coming – it's bound to rain"

"It's all the monsoons we've been having"

"I see there's no danger of drought here"

"Close the door or you'll let the goldfish out"

"Typical! You make it all the way to the front door and then summer's over"

"I'm slightly regretting buying the snow plough now"

"Get the sunloungers out – the Met office have forecast snow"

"Oh look, the first penguin of spring"

"They predicted a slight thaw, not a heat wave"

"It's nice to get the extra hour of light to watch the snow"

"It's so cold outside I rather felt for him"

"Now can we put the heating on?"

"Any idea whether the bin men took our rubbish or not?"

"What luck! I've found a bit of grit in my eye"

Freezing Britain faces grit shortage

"I don't want your jewellery, where's your salt pot?"